Written by Heather Dakota
Illustrated and designed by Sandra Bruner

Copyright © 2016 Scholastic Inc.

SCHOLASTIC and Tangerine Press and associated logos are trademarks of Scholastic Inc.

Published by Tangerine Press, an imprint of
Scholastic Inc., 557 Broadway, New York, NY 10012

Scholastic Canada Ltd.; Markham, Ontario
Scholastic Australia Pty. Ltd; Gosford NSW
Scholastic New Zealand Ltd.; Greenmount, Auckland

10 9 8 7 6 5 4 3 2 1

ISBN: 978-0-545-86391-9

Printed and bound in Jiaxing, China

an imprint of
■SCHOLASTIC
www.scholastic.com

Photo credits:

Book Photos ©: cover, 2, 3: Ron Kimball/KimballStock; 6 top, 6 center top, 6 bottom: GlobalP/iStockphoto; 6 center bottom, 7: Ron Kimball/KimballStock; 12: WilleeCole/iStockphoto; 13: 101cats/iStockphoto; 18: Brian Kimball/KimballStock; 19 top: UroshPetrovic/iStockphoto; 19 center top: scorpp/iStockphoto; 19 center bottom, 19 bottom: GlobalP/iStockphoto; 21 top left: Czanner/iStockphoto; 21 top center left: Justin Horrocks/iStockphoto; 21 bottom center left: Anna Utekhina/Dreamstime; 21 bottom left: Chepko/iStockphoto; 21 right: Photoshopped/iStockphoto; 22-23: AVTG/iStockphoto; 22 inset: Klein-Hubert/KimballStock; 24-25: Figure8Photos/iStockphoto; 25 inset: Lynn M. Stone/KimballStock; 26, 27: Ermolaev Alexander/Shutterstock, Inc.; 28: 101cats/iStockphoto; 29: EEI_Tony/iStockphoto; 32 top: UroshPetrovic/iStockphoto; 32 center: Lilun_Li/iStockphoto; 32 bottom: spxChrome/iStockphoto; 33: Ermolaev Alexander/Shutterstock, Inc.; 38 top left: MishelVerini/Shutterstock, Inc.; 38 top right: cynoclub/iStockphoto; 38 bottom left: EEI_Tony/iStockphoto; 38 bottom right: Gary Randall/KimballStock; 39 top left: IrinaK/Shutterstock, Inc.; 39 top right: otsphoto/Shutterstock, Inc.; 39 center left: Bartkowski/Shutterstock, Inc.; 39 center right: suemack/iStockphoto; 39 bottom left: Gita Kulinitch Studio/Shutterstock, Inc.; 39 bottom right: Okssi68/iStockphoto; 40 top left: damedeeso/iStockphoto; 40 top right: Eric Isselee/Shutterstock, Inc.; 40 bottom left: diane39/iStockphoto; 40 bottom right: Annette Shaff/Shutterstock, Inc.; 41 top left: gurinaleksandr/Shutterstock, Inc.; 41 top right: hannadarzy/Shutterstock, Inc.; 41 bottom left: Annette Shaff/Shutterstock, Inc.; 41 bottom right: quangpraha/iStockphoto; 50: Lilun_Li/iStockphoto; 63: vvvita/Shutterstock, Inc.; 65: Eric Isselee/Shutterstock, Inc.; 70: JStaley401/Shutterstock, Inc.; 73: Renata Apanaviciene/Shutterstock, Inc.; 76 top: Zoran Kolundzija/iStockphoto; 76 center top, 76 center bottom: GlobalP/iStockphoto; 76 bottom: KeithSzafranski/iStockphoto; 77 top: picstodisc/iStockphoto; 77 center: Kaphoto/iStockphoto; 77 bottom: rohojamagic/iStockphoto; 78: funebre/iStockphoto; 79: Paffy69/iStockphoto; 82: Rosa Jay/Shutterstock, Inc.; 86: mrPliskin/iStockphoto; 87: kuban_girl/iStockphoto; 89 top, 89 center bottom: damedeeso/iStockphoto; 89 center top, 89 bottom, 90 top, 90 center bottom: kuban_girl/iStockphoto; 90 center top, 90 bottom: damedeeso/iStockphoto; 92 left: Nikada/iStockphoto; 92 right: kuban_girl/iStockphoto; 93 left: haoliang/iStockphoto; 93 right: damedeeso/iStockphoto; 100: Liliya Kulianionak/Shutterstock, Inc.; 101: ktaylorg/iStockphoto; 102: Yoshio Tomii/KimballStock; 103: Ermolaev Alexander/Shutterstock, Inc.

Sticker Sheet Photos ©: Brian Kimball/KimballStock; UroshPetrovic/iStockphoto; Justin Horrocks/iStockphoto; spxChrome/iStockphoto; Ermolaev Alexander/Shutterstock, Inc.; Okssi68/iStockphoto; diane39/iStockphoto; vvvita/Shutterstock, Inc.; Eric Isselee/Shutterstock, Inc.; Renata Apanaviciene/Shutterstock, Inc.; mrPliskin/iStockphoto; kuban_girl/iStockphoto; damedeeso/iStockphoto; Liliya Kulianionak/Shutterstock, Inc.

Your pets are your best friends. But are puppies or kitties your favorite? Dig into this book to discover quizzes, games, and a ton of furry fun. Find out which one should be your favorite fur-ever friend.

Pet Picker

Is a puppy or a kitty right for you?
Follow the trail to pick the perfect pet.

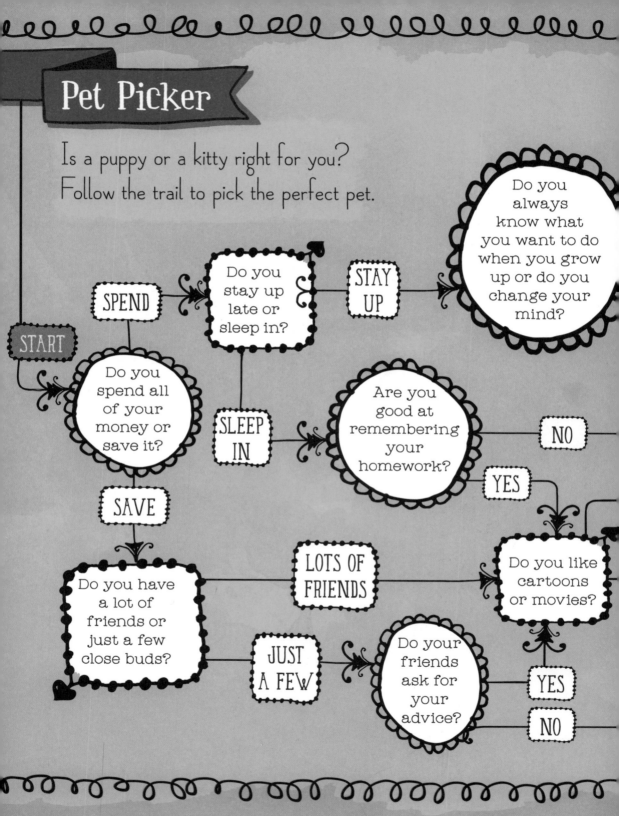

START

SPEND

Do you spend all of your money or save it?

SAVE

Do you stay up late or sleep in?

STAY UP

SLEEP IN

Do you always know what you want to do when you grow up or do you change your mind?

Are you good at remembering your homework?

NO

YES

Do you have a lot of friends or just a few close buds?

LOTS OF FRIENDS

JUST A FEW

Do your friends ask for your advice?

Do you like cartoons or movies?

YES

YES

NO

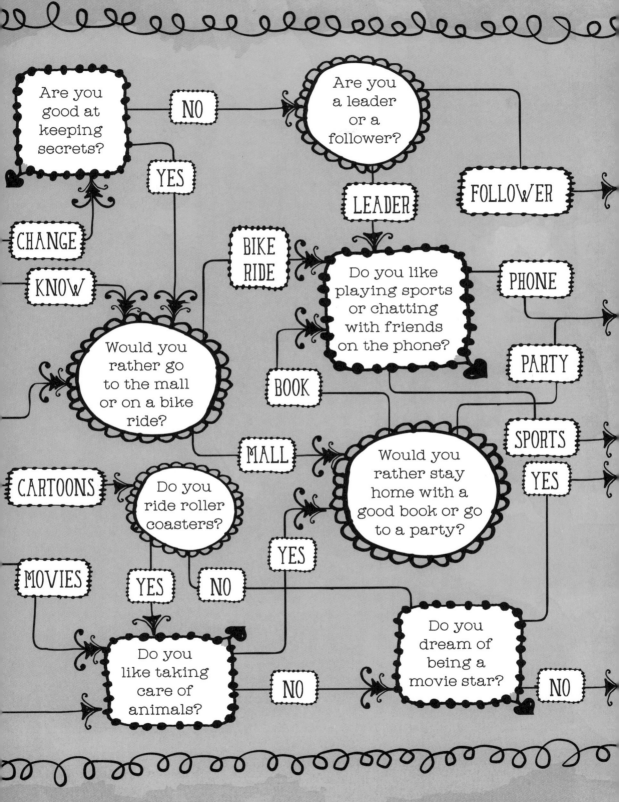

Are you good at keeping secrets?

NO → Are you a leader or a follower?

YES

CHANGE

KNOW

LEADER

FOLLOWER

BIKE RIDE

Do you like playing sports or chatting with friends on the phone?

PHONE

PARTY

BOOK

Would you rather go to the mall or on a bike ride?

MALL

SPORTS

YES

Would you rather stay home with a good book or go to a party?

CARTOONS

Do you ride roller coasters?

YES

MOVIES

YES   NO

Do you like taking care of animals?

NO

Do you dream of being a movie star?

NO

Follow the arrows from pages 4 and 5.

FINAL ANSWERS

PUPPY

Your perfect pet is a puppy! You'll be best friends.

KITTEN

You are a busy bee! You'll do well with a kitten.

BOTH

You would do well with a puppy or a kitten, or maybe one of each. Which one would you like best?

NEITHER

Are you not really into the whole puppy or kitten thing? There are a lot of other pets that you might like. Maybe a horse, mouse, rabbit, or snake is more your style.

The Puppy List

Check off all of the things that are puppy-perfect for you.

- ◯ Long hair
- ✓ Short hair
- ✓ Curly hair
- ◯ Needs exercise
- ✓ Likes to sit in my lap
- ✓ Super-cute
- ✓ Good watchdog
- ✓ Does tricks
- ✓ House-trained
- ✓ Very active
- ✓ Allergy-free
- ✓ Blue eyes
- ◯ Brown eyes

- ◯ Different-colored eyes
- ✓ Lives inside
- ◯ Lives outside
- ◯ Sleeps in my room
- ✓ Sleeps in my bed
- ✓ High maintenance
- ◯ Low maintenance
- ◯ Sleeps a lot
- ◯ My constant companion
- ✓ Purebred
- ◯ Mixed breed
- ◯ Hybrid (puppy from two different purebred dogs)

- ☑ Adopted
- ☑ Free
- ☑ Small dog
- ◯ Medium dog
- ◯ Large dog
- ☑ Tiny dog
- ◯ Obedient
- ◯ Likes to roam in the country
- ◯ Likes to stay home
- ☑ Happy
- ☑ Confident

- ☑ Smiley
- ☑ Tail wagger
- ◯ Barks a lot
- ☑ Pretty quiet
- ☑ Smart
- ☑ Just your average dog
- ◯ Police dog
- ◯ Hound
- ◯ Sporting dog
- ◯ Terrier
- ◯ Working dog
- ◯ Herding dog

The Kitty List

Check off all of the things that are kitty-rrific for you.

- ○ Long hair
- ⊘ Short hair
- ○ Curly hair
- ⊘ High maintenance
- ○ Low maintenance
- ☑ Allergy-free
- ○ Needs a lot of grooming
- ☑ Doesn't need grooming
- ☑ Litter-box trained
- ○ Lives inside
- ☑ Lives outside
- ☑ Sleeps in my room
- ☑ Sleeps in my bed

- ☑ Needs a lot of exercise
- ☑ Likes to sit in my lap
- ☑ Super-cute
- ☑ Does tricks
- ☑ Very active
- ☑ Blue eyes
- ○ Green eyes
- ○ Yellow eyes
- ☑ Different-colored eyes
- ☑ Sleeps a lot
- ○ My constant companion
- ○ Purebred
- ⊘ Mixed breed

- ☑ Adopted
- ☑ Free
- ☑ Small cat
- ◯ Medium cat
- ◯ Large cat
- ◯ Obedient
- ☑ Likes to roam
- ◯ Likes to stay home
- ☑ Happy
- ☑ Confident
- ◯ Vocal
- ☑ Pretty quiet
- ☑ Smiley

- ◯ Shows affection
- ☑ Playful
- ☑ Smart
- ☑ Just your average cat
- ☑ Exotic
- ☑ Unusual features
- ☑ Striped
- ◯ Spotted
- ☑ One color
- ◯ Two colors
- ◯ Three colors
- ◯ Tabby

Furry Friend Playdate

Help the kitten find her puppy friend.

Answer key is on page 110.

Cat Breed Word Search

Find the cat breeds. They might be forward, backward, up, down, or diagonal. If the name is two words, there will not be a space between the words in the search.

```
X N Y H P S R C I U A E S V W W Q D Z J
B R Y G T M U N O O B I Z S K N N R S L
I R K E P O I A R R A D R I A C H U P L
B C A Z J K Y I M M N L B I A X G S I J
B W R G H T E G E N Y I S N N M M S X P
K W B C D N U S E A A R S I V A A I I J
C F N E T O E R B R E I W H T N E A E L
L U Z A N Y L Y K P D E T A R X Y N B J
M N L C A G S L W I L L G P D E C B O E
Y T V B K S A S M V S J Q M Y T X L B I
H C M Y I S D L M P Q H O R C G U U J J
M O S N V V I A X A I C V D S R E E N B
B O I T Y W I O R M Q R H A W U T D W X
U A A L E N C U A O S L U A N O V Z N H
N I H N E I P L H S Y R X Q R M Z Z H F
R R V C C A A J D L O F H S I T T O C S
U E O A G Y R F X N A M R I B C R H A A
I O T N A Q K V U K O R A T E C X E D G
N J I N Z G F J G L I O P W O U N W U G
P S N M P P G A B F B F V Q D E W S X X
```

Abyssinian	Chartreux
Korat	Ocicat
Ragdoll	Singapura
Bengal	Cornish Rex
Maine Coon	Oriental
Russian Blue	Sphynx
Birman	Egyptian Mau
Manx	Persian
Scottish Fold	Toyger
Bombay	Himalayan
Munchkin	Pixie Bob
Siamese	Turkish Van

Answer key is on page 110.

Dog Breed Word Search

Find the dog breeds. They might be forward, backward, up, down, or diagonal. If the name is two words, there will not be a space between the words in the search.

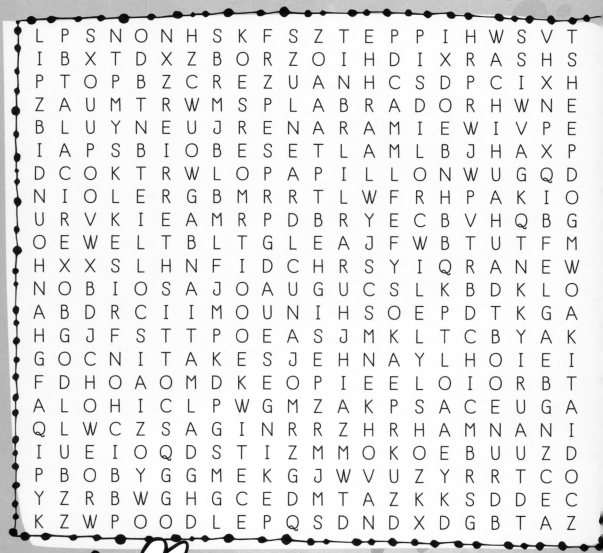

```
L P S N O N H S K F S Z T E P P I H W S V T
I B X T D X Z B O R Z O I H D I X R A S H S
P T O P B Z C R E Z U A N H C S D P C I X H
Z A U M T R W M S P L A B R A D O R H W N E
B L U Y N E U J R E N A R A M I E W I V P E
I A P S B I O B E S E T L A M L B J H A X P
D C O K T R W L O P A P I L L O N W U G Q D
N I O L E R G B M R R T L W F R H P A K I O
U R V K I E A M R P D B R Y E C B V H Q B G
O E W E L T B L T G L E A J F W B T U T F M
H X X S L H N F I D C H R S Y I Q R A N E W
N O B I O S A J O A U G U C S L K B D K L O
A B D R C I I M O U N I H S O E P D T K G A
H G J F S T T P O E A S J M K L T C B Y A K
G O C N I T A K E S J E H N A Y L H O I E I
F D H O A O M D K E O P I E E L O I O R B T
A L O H I C L P W G M Z A K P S A C E U G A
Q L W C Z S A G I N R R Z H R H A M N A N I
I U E I O Q D S T I Z M M O K O E B U U Z D
P B O B Y G G M E K G J W V U Z Y R R T C O
Y Z R B W G H G C E D M T A Z K K S D D E C
K Z W P O O D L E P Q S D N D X D G B T A Z
```

Afghan Hound	Beagle
Bulldog	Dalmatian
Papillon	Scottish Terrier
Akita	Bichon Frise
Chihuahua	Husky
Pekingese	Sheepdog
Australian Shepherd	Border Collie
Chow	Labrador
Poodle	Weimaraner
Basenji	Borzoi
Collie	Malamute
Puli	Whippet
Basset Hound	Boxer
Corgi	Maltese
Schnauzer	Yorkie

Answer key is on page 110.

Pup-arazzi

What does your fashion style say about the type of dog that is right for you? Take the quiz and find out.

1 AFTER SCHOOL, YOU'LL BE ...
- ○ a. Picking flowers in your garden
- ✓ b. Going to the mall
- ○ c. Playing sports
- ○ d. Going on a hike

2 YOUR FAVORITE EXERCISE IS ...
- ○ a. Yoga
- ✓ b. Dancing
- ○ c. Kickboxing
- ○ d. Riding bikes

3 YOUR FAVORITE FOOD IS ...
- ✓ a. Dessert!
- ○ b. A yummy salad
- ○ c. Fruits, nuts and energy bars
- ○ d. Anything that can be made in under 15 minutes

4 IF YOUR LIFE WAS A MOVIE, IT WOULD BE ...
- ○ a. A romance
- ○ b. A drama
- ○ c. A comedy
- ✓ d. An action adventure

5 THE STYLE YOU LOVE THE MOST IS ...
- ✓ a. Fresh and sweet
- ○ b. Spicy and hot
- ○ c. Sporty and fun
- ○ d. Mysterious and unique

6 THE EXOTIC PET YOU'D LOVE TO HAVE ...
- ○ a. Macaw
- ○ b. Cheetah
- ✓ c. Monkey
- ○ d. Wolf

7 YOUR FRIENDS WOULD DESCRIBE YOU AS ...
- ✓ a. Artsy
- ○ b. Rad
- ○ c. Athletic
- ○ d. Geeky

8 YOUR FAVORITE SUBJECT IN SCHOOL IS ...
- ○ a. Music
- ✓ b. Art
- ○ c. P.E.
- ○ d. Geography

ANSWERS

MOVIE STAR PUPPY!
MOSTLY A's

There are stars in your eyes and your puppy should look the part. Consider dogs like the Pomeranian, Pug, or Poodle for your star-studded lineup.

GLAM PUP!
MOSTLY B's

You are a fashion star all the way. A puppy would be a great accessory, so look at dogs like the Chihuahua, Yorkie, or Chinese Crested for that bit of glam.

SPORTY POOCH!
MOSTLY C's

Being active is your thing, so your dog should be sporty, too. Dogs like the Labrador Retriever, Australian Shepherd, and Border Collie would be able to keep up with you.

ADVENTURE DOG!
MOSTLY D's

You need a dog that can keep you company on all of your adventures. Hardy pups like the German Shepherd, St. Bernard, or Husky would be perfect pets.

Kitty Couture

What does your fashion style say about the type of cat that is right for you? Take the quiz and find out.

1 WHAT DO YOU PREFER TO DO ON THE WEEKENDS?
- ○ a. Stay home to read a book
- ✓ b. Go to the mall with friends
- ○ c. Go to the parks
- ○ d. Go on a bike ride

2 HOW MANY CLOSE FRIENDS DO YOU HAVE?
- ○ a. 1 or 2
- ○ b. At least 10
- ○ c. 3 or 4
- ✓ d. Enough for a team

3 HOW MUCH DO YOU LIKE TAKING RISKS?
- ○ a. Not so much
- ○ b. Only with my friends
- ○ c. Nothing to it!
- ✓ d. Only if you dare me

4 DOES IT TAKE YOU A LONG TIME TO DECIDE WHAT TO WEAR?
- ○ a. No, I'm super-quick
- ✓ b. Yes, sometimes an hour
- ○ c. Only if I'm going out
- ○ d. T-shirt and jeans, right?

5 WHAT IS YOUR FAVORITE PART OF THE FASHION WORLD?
- ○ a. Clothing designer
- ○ b. Model
- ✓ c. Makeup artist
- ○ d. Eh, not my thing

6 WHAT IS YOUR FAVORITE OUTDOOR ACTIVITY?
- ○ a. Do I have to?
- ○ b. Whatever my friends are doing
- ○ c. Skateboarding solo or with my friends
- ✓ d. Mountain biking

7 HOW DO YOU LIKE TO STUDY?
- ✓ a. By myself
- ○ b. With all of my friends
- ○ c. Outside
- ○ d. Library

8 HOW DO YOU LIKE TO WEAR YOUR HAIR?
- ○ a. Combed, but that's about it
- ○ b. I spend a lot of time on my hair
- ○ c. Natural
- ✓ d. Ponytail

ANSWERS

COOL CAT!

You like to keep it down to earth. You keep your life calm and unstressed. With your laid-back style, a Ragdoll would be the perfect kitty for you.

MOSTLY A's

POSH!

You are a glam girl and the center of attention. With your dramatic, flashy style, a Persian would be the perfect accessory.

MOSTLY B's

WILD CHILD!

You go with your gut instincts and create your own trends. With your outrageous style, a Bengal would be perfect for you.

MOSTLY C's

BUSY BEE!

You have a busy schedule but not a lot of time. You like to keep your wardrobe simple, so the best cat for you is a Siamese.

MOSTLY D's

Find the kitty hidden in the picture.

Answer key is on page 111.

Dog Finder

There is a puppy hidden somewhere in the image.
Find it and give it a good home.

Answer key is on page 111.

What are the puppy and kitten saying to each other? Add thought or speech bubbles from the sticker sheet for a bit of fun.

What are your pets trying
to tell you? Add thought
or speech bubbles from
the sticker sheet.

Welcome to My House!

Which animal will rule in your house? Take the quiz to find out.

START

YOUR FRIDAY NIGHT PLANS INCLUDE:

Some TV watching

Hanging with friends at the mall

YOU HAVE A SLEEPOVER AT YOUR HOUSE BUT WAKE UP EARLY. WHAT DO YOU DO?

Feed the cat

YOUR FRIEND CALLS TO ASK YOU TO HANG OUT. YOU SAY:

Sure, the cat won't mind

Sorry, I have to give the dog a bath

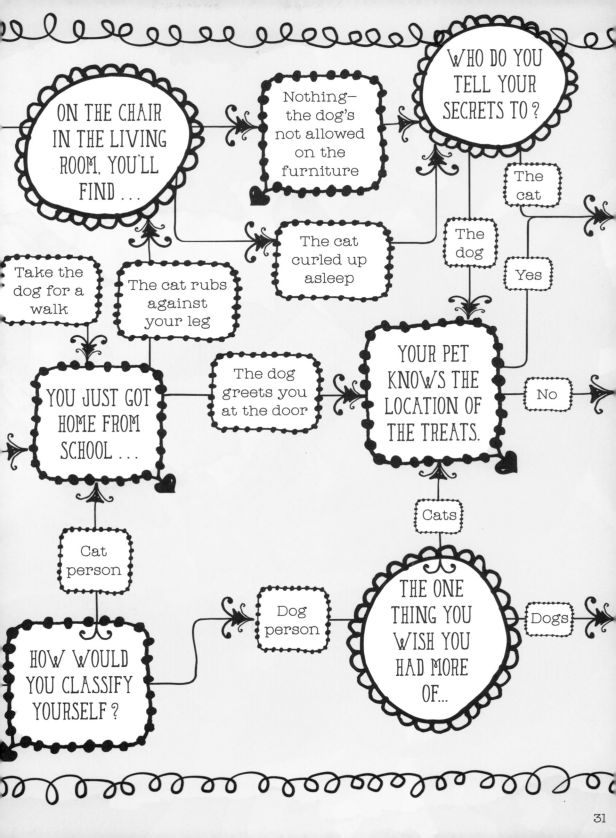

ON THE CHAIR IN THE LIVING ROOM, YOU'LL FIND ...

Nothing—the dog's not allowed on the furniture

WHO DO YOU TELL YOUR SECRETS TO ?

The cat

The dog

The cat curled up asleep

Yes

Take the dog for a walk

The cat rubs against your leg

YOU JUST GOT HOME FROM SCHOOL ...

The dog greets you at the door

YOUR PET KNOWS THE LOCATION OF THE TREATS.

No

Cat person

Cats

HOW WOULD YOU CLASSIFY YOURSELF ?

Dog person

THE ONE THING YOU WISH YOU HAD MORE OF...

Dogs

Follow the arrows from pages 30 and 31.

ANSWERS

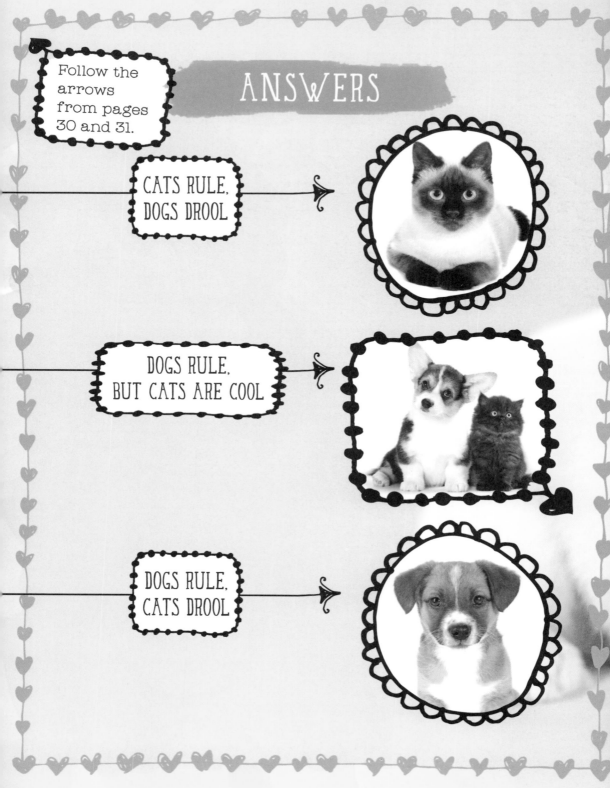

CATS RULE, DOGS DROOL

DOGS RULE, BUT CATS ARE COOL

DOGS RULE, CATS DROOL

This or That?

Circle the "This" or "That" you like best.

CATS
or
DOGS

BIG
or
SMALL

ON YOUR LAP
or
OUTSIDE

MEOW
or
WOOF

GOOD HEARING
or
GOOD EYESIGHT

PLAYFUL
or
LAZY

ACTIVE
or
CHILL

BOSSY
or
EAGER to PLEASE

34

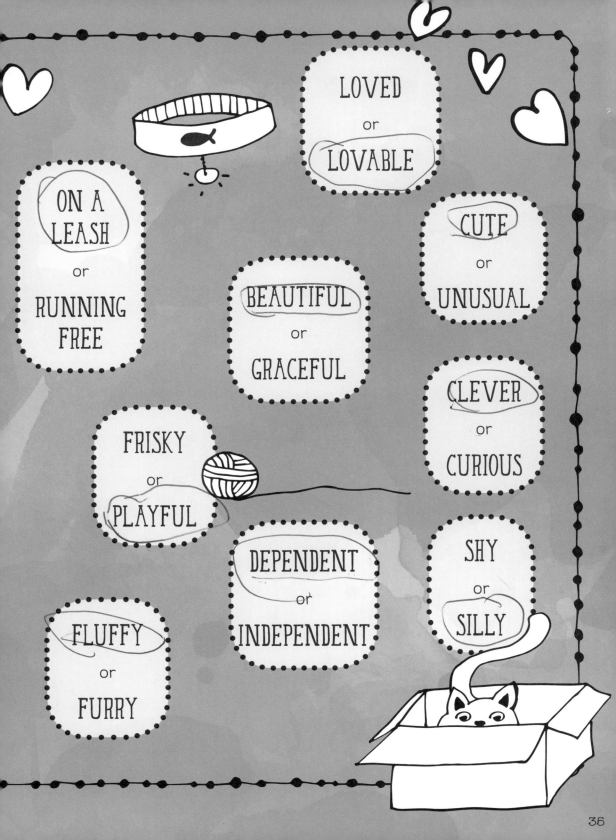

LOVED
or
LOVABLE

ON A
LEASH
or
RUNNING
FREE

CUTE
or
UNUSUAL

BEAUTIFUL
or
GRACEFUL

CLEVER
or
CURIOUS

FRISKY
or
PLAYFUL

DEPENDENT
or
INDEPENDENT

SHY
or
SILLY

FLUFFY
or
FURRY

REGAL
or
REBELLIOUS

SHINY
or
SCRUFFY

GOOFY
or
ROWDY

LOYAL
or
SPONTANEOUS

SNUGGLY
or
DARING

SPOILED
ROTTEN
or
STANDOFFISH

TOUGH
or
SWEET

AGILE
or
CLUMSY

PUREBRED
or
MIXED BREED

TABBY
or
SPOTTED

PEOPLE-
FRIENDLY

or

DETACHED

NEEDY

or

MOODY

DEMANDING

or

DEVOTED

ATTITUDE

or

FUNNY

PICK UP POO

or

CLEAN OUT
KITTY LITTER

GROWL

or

HISS

TAIL-WAGGING

or

LEG-RUBBING

POUNCING

or

BOUNCING

MISCHIEVOUS

or

WELL-BEHAVED

What Does the Cat Say?

Use the speech bubble stickers to add funny lines to the kitty images. What are they saying to each other?

What Does the Dog Say?

Use the speech bubble stickers to add funny lines to the puppy images. What are they saying to each other?

Use the prompts to finish the drawings on these pages.

Give this puppy a head and a tail.

What kind of art would a dog
want to see in a museum?

Add some puppy
friends to this
birthday party.

Kitty Kraze

Add some kitty friends, flowers, and paw prints.
What does your kitty need?

Give this kitty a head and a tail.

If a cat could buy a cupcake,
what would it look like?

Add some kitty friends to this play date.

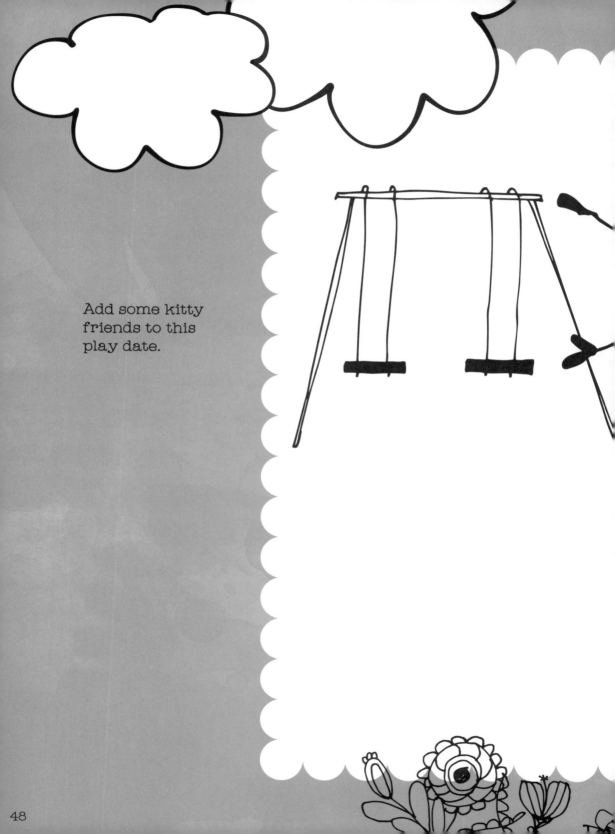

Things I Know Are True

1
2
3
4
5
6
7
8

Things I Know Are True

ABOUT DOGS

1

2

3

4

5

6

7

8

Furry Friend Gallery

Add photos of your furry friends to this gallery. If you don't have pets, draw or collage images that you find.

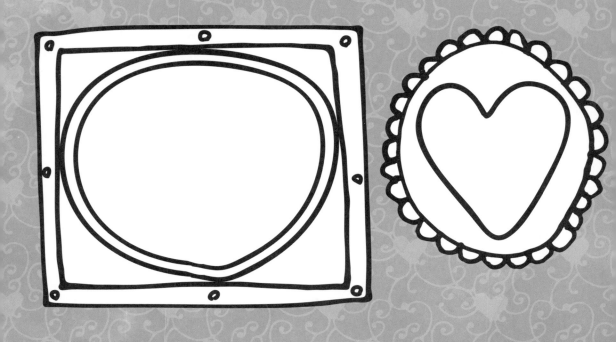

Best Kitty Names

1

2

3

4

5

6

7

8

9

10

11

12

13

14

15

16

Best Puppy Names

1.

2.

3.

4.

5.

6.

7.

8.

9

10

11

12

13

14

15

16

What's Your Kitty Mood?

Hold your pencil or pen on these pages. Close your eyes and move your pen or pencil back and forth until a friend says "Stop." Where you land is your kitty mood for today.

HAPPY

BLANK

SAD

UPSET

INFATUATED

FLIRTY

NERDY

ANNOYED

HIPSTER

GLAD

PEACEFUL

CHEERY

EXCITED

SURPRISED

CONCERNED

BUMMED OUT

STRESSED

EDGY

GRUMPY

What's Your Puppy Mood?

Hold your pencil or pen on these pages. Close your eyes and move your pen or pencil back and forth until a friend says, "Stop." Where you land is your puppy mood for today.

DREAMY

CONTENT

BLAH

CRUSHED

FRUSTRATED

HAPPY

CRABBY

HUFFY

CHEERY

SHOCKED

NERVOUS

STUNNED

UPTIGHT

CALM

DAZZLED

LAID-BACK

DETERMINED

SAD

ENERGETIC

It's a Dog's Life

Write down what you think your dog does all day while you're at school. If you don't have a dog, pretend you do.

AFTER YOU LEAVE FOR SCHOOL

MORNING

LUNCH

AFTERNOON

RIGHT BEFORE YOU GET HOME

It's a Cat's Life

Write down what you think your cat does all day while you're at school. If you don't have a cat, pretend you do.

AFTER YOU LEAVE FOR SCHOOL

MORNING

LUNCH

AFTERNOON

RIGHT BEFORE YOU GET HOME

The Wild Animal Quiz

What wild animal are you? Take the quiz and find out.

1 WHAT ADJECTIVE WOULD BEST DESCRIBE YOU?
- ○ a. Graceful
- ○ b. Kind
- ○ c. Beautiful
- ○ d. Strong
- ○ e. Friendly
- ○ f. Shy
- ○ g. Playful

2 WHAT QUALITY DO YOU ADMIRE IN OTHERS?
- ○ a. Loyalty
- ○ b. Kindness
- ○ c. Beauty
- ○ d. Strength
- ○ e. Bravery
- ○ f. Spontaneity
- ○ g. Outgoing

3 WHAT DO YOU LIKE TO EAT?
- ○ a. Meat!
- ○ b. Only veggies and fruit
- ○ c. I like meat and vegetables
- ○ d. Fish
- ○ e. Any kind of food is good
- ○ f. Junk food
- ○ g. Dessert

4 WHAT'S YOUR FAVORITE SEASON?
- ○ a. Winter
- ○ b. Summer
- ○ c. Fall
- ○ d. Spring
- ○ e. A combination of two
- ○ f. Don't really care one way or the other
- ○ g. All seasons

5 HOW MUCH DO YOU LIKE ATTENTION?
- ○ a. I like the attention
- ○ b. No, thank you!
- ○ c. I don't really like being in the spotlight
- ○ d. It depends
- ○ e. It's awesome!
- ○ f. Don't need it
- ○ g. Eh, it's okay

6 WHAT IS YOUR FAVORITE KIND OF PET?
- ○ a. An unusual one
- ○ b. Cat
- ○ c. Dog
- ○ d. Cat and dog
- ○ e. A small dog
- ○ f. An exotic cat
- ○ g. Something small, soft, and cuddly

7 HOW ACTIVE ARE YOU?
- ○ a. Is it nap time yet?
- ○ b. Once in a while
- ○ c. Never
- ○ d. Sometimes
- ○ e. I enjoy the outdoors
- ○ f. Only if I have to
- ○ g. All the time

8 WHAT'S YOUR FAVORITE COLOR?
- ○ a. Orange
- ○ b. Black
- ○ c. White
- ○ d. Gray
- ○ e. Brown
- ○ f. A combo of colors
- ○ g. Blue

The answers are . . .

MOSTLY A's

YOU ARE A TIGER FOR SURE.

This means you are strong and brave but can be a bit aggressive. However, you love life. There is nothing that can stop you from getting what you want. Your tigerlike attitude will help you tackle any challenge that you face.

MOSTLY B's

A CHIMP IS THE WILD ANIMAL YOU'D BE.

You're smart and energetic. Playing with your friends and family is very important to you. You might be a bit of a prankster with a good sense of humor. Climbing trees might be your thing.

MOSTLY C's

AN OWL IS THE ANIMAL THAT YOU'RE LIKE.

Owls have the power to see in the dark. Do you like to stay up late, and are you a bit of a "night owl"? You probably like to explore mysteries and your own creativity. But make sure you get enough sleep. Maybe take a nap!

MOSTLY D's

THERE IS NO DOUBT THAT A WOLF IS WHAT YOU'D BE.

You go by your gut instincts most of the time and like your freedom. Your emotions are right on the surface and that's okay. You are extremely intelligent and deal with all kinds of important things. And there is nothing more important to you than your friends and family.

MOSTLY E's

A BEAR IS THE ANIMAL THAT YOU'RE MOST LIKE.

You kind of like being alone and spending time resting, reading, or just being quiet. But you are strong when you need to be and like to lead if you can. You're respected by everyone who knows you.

MOSTLY F's

A DEER IS THE WILD ANIMAL THAT YOU'RE MOST LIKE.

You are a gentle person who is kind and loving to others. Your life is full of grace and heart. Taking time in the peace and silence of nature is right up your alley.

MOSTLY G's

A DOLPHIN IS WHAT YOU'D BE.

Your playful nature is a joy to everyone, but your intelligence is off the charts! You love hanging with your friends and family, and would do anything for them. You probably like water, too.

Puppy & Kitten Tally

Keep a running tally of the cats or dogs you see in these different places. Check a box each time you see a cat or dog. Who has the most on your tally cards?

THE CAT TALLY

	Grocery store		At your friend's house
	School		On vacation
	The park		The mall
	Doctor's office		Dance class
	In your front yard		Soccer practice

THE DOG TALLY

	Grocery store
	School
	The park
	Doctor's office
	In your front yard
	At your friend's house
	On vacation
	The mall
	Dance class
	Soccer practice

What's Your Furry Friend Name?

If you were a dog or a cat, what would your name be? Look at the charts on these pages. Use your birth date to find your puppy or kitty first name and your birth month to find your furry friend last name. Have all of your friends try it, too!

BIRTH DATES & FIRST NAMES

1 Cupcake	2 Maisy	3 Angel	4 Buttons	5 Lily	6 Cody
7 Spot	8 Charlie	9 Max	10 Peanut	11 Buddy	12 Kiki	13 Jack

7 Spot	8 Charlie	9 Max	10 Peanut	11 Buddy	12 Kiki	13 Jack
14 Snowball	15 Cooper	16 Misty	17 Bella	18 Mittens	19 Ellie	20 Daisy
21 Patches	22 Molly	23 Coco	24 Ruby	25 Poppy	26 Buttercup	27 Cookie
28 Roo	29 Ginger	30 Princess	31 Bailey			

BIRTH MONTHS & LAST NAMES

JANUARY	Barksalot
FEBRUARY	Fluffington
MARCH	Boneham
APRIL	Snuggleball
MAY	O'Drool
JUNE	Clawford
JULY	Woofgang
AUGUST	Pawthorne
SEPTEMBER	Ravenpaw
OCTOBER	Waggins
NOVEMBER	Picatso
DECEMBER	Pupstable

Fetch

Help the puppy find his bone.

Answer key is on page 112.

All About My Puppy

Write all about your puppy or the one you really want.

_____

_____

_____

_____

_____

_____

_____

_____

_____

_____

_____

_____

_____

_____

_____

_____

_____

_____

_____

_____

_____

_____

All About My Kitten

Tell about the kitten you have or the one you really want.

Finish the Story

Tell the rest of the story. Where did they go? How did they get there? Did they stop anywhere? What was the weather like? What did they see? Who found them?

A PUPPY & A KITTEN
WENT ON AN
ADVENTURE ...

Kitten Word Scramble

The kitten just scattered all of the letters.
Can you help unscramble the words?

1 anry..

2 lffuyf..

3 rpur..

4 lhrialba..

5 raspine...

6 ooblcri...

7 lacoic..

8 batby...

9 mweo..

10 madrpepe...

11 rcriera...

12 fnleei..

13 lnio..

14 tgire..

15 caatpn...

16 etcixo...

17 olxretbit..

18 ueosm...

Answer key is on page 112.

Puppy Word Scramble

Oh, no! The puppy just jumbled up all of the letters.
Can you help unscramble the words?

1 ofwo..

2 brak..

3 neob..

4 hhauhaicu..

5 loeopd..

6 ueerdpbr..

7 mtut..

8 gmriongo..

9 urryf..

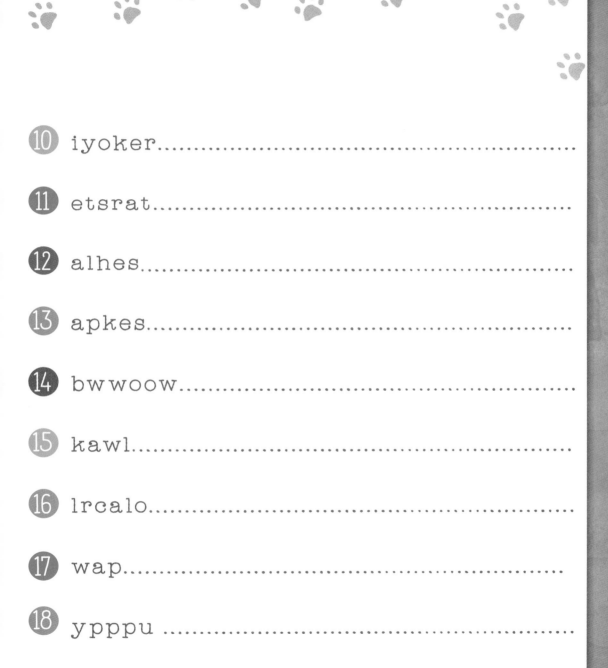

10 iyoker...

11 etsrat...

12 alhes..

13 apkes..

14 bwwoow...

15 kawl...

16 lrcalo...

17 wap..

18 ypppu ....

Answer key is on page 112.

Nothing but the Truth

Circle the **T** for true or the **F** for false for the following statements.

I would swim with a dolphin.	T	F
I do not eat meat.	T	F
I have a cat.	T	F
I don't like cats.	T	F
I have a dog.	T	F
I don't like dogs.	T	F
A parent feeds my pet.	T	F
I want a monkey.	T	F
I have held a snake.	T	F
Wolves don't scare me.	T	F
I've seen a bear in the wild.	T	F
Birds are my thing.	T	F
I can whistle like a bird.	T	F
I have ridden a horse.	T	F
I have ridden an elephant.	T	F
I'd like to ride a camel.	T	F

I've been on an African safari.	T	F
I would swim with sharks.	T	F
I like to fish.	T	F
I like to climb trees.	T	F
My dog can do tricks.	T	F
I like napping, like my cat.	T	F
I prefer the cold of winter, like a penguin.	T	F
My cat chases a light.	T	F
Insects are super-cool.	T	F
I have held a frog.	T	F
Bird-watching is fun.	T	F
I've seen a whale in the wild.	T	F
I pay attention to details.	T	F
Playing is my favorite thing to do.	T	F
I could never wear fur.	T	F
I have purebred pets.	T	F
My favorite pet is small and furry.	T	F
My pets are adopted.	T	F

Dear Puppies and Kittens ...

Write a letter to all of the cats and dogs
that are waiting to be adopted.

Selfie Puppy & Kitty

Take some photos of you and your dog or cat. Paste them here.

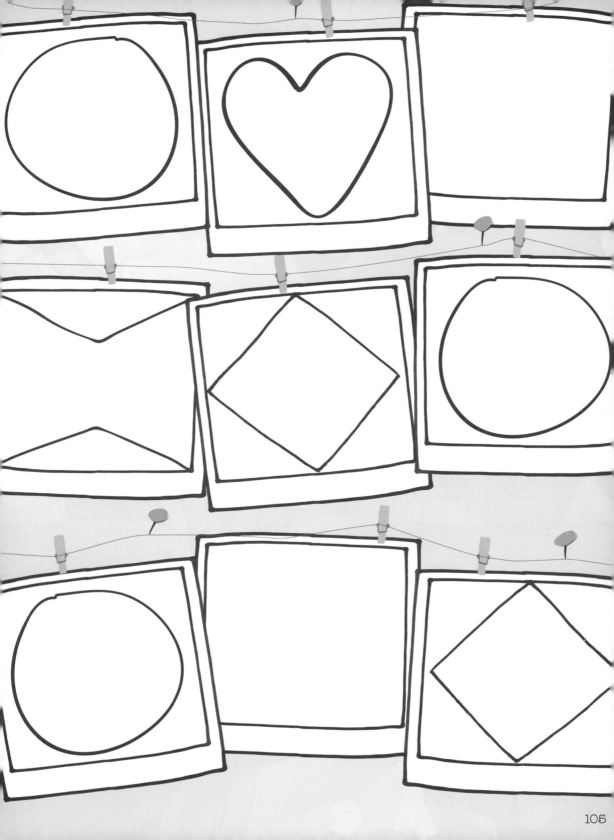

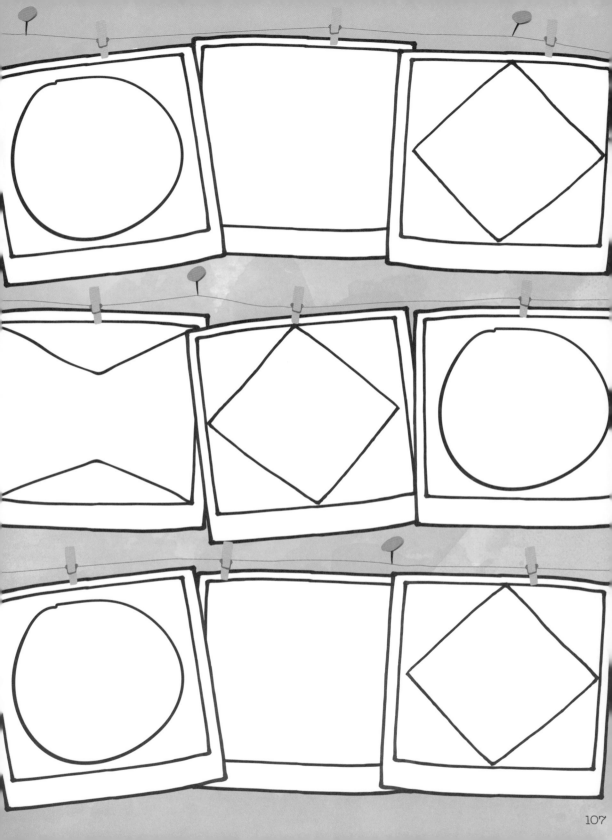

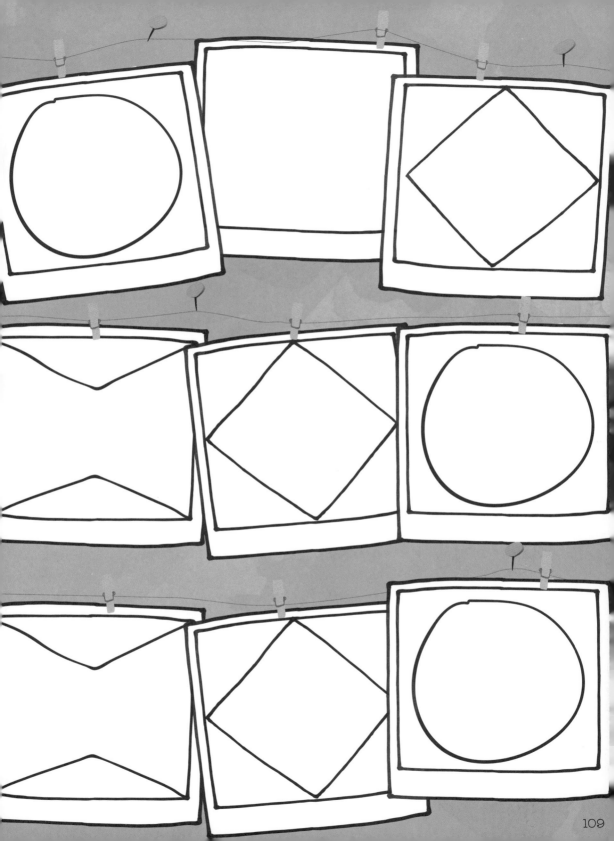

Answers

Pages 12–13
Furry Friend Playdate

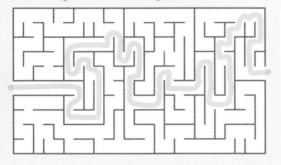

Pages 14–15
Cat Breed Word Search

```
X N Y H P S R C I U A E S V W W Q D Z J
B R Y G T M U N O O B I Z S K N N R S L
I R K E P O I A R R A D R I A C H U P L
B C A Z J K Y I M M N L B I A X G S I J
B W R G H T E G E N Y I S N N M M S X P
K W B C D N U S E A A R S I V A A I I J
C F N E T O E R B R E I W H T N E A E L
L U Z A N Y L Y K P D E T A R X Y N B J
M N L C A G S L W I L L G P D E C B O E
Y T V B K S A S M V S J Q M Y T X L B I
H C M Y I S D L M P Q H O R C G U U J D
M O S N V V I A X A I C V O S R E E N B
B O I T Y W I O R M Q R H A W U T D W X
U A A L E N C U A O S L U A N O V Z N H
N I H N E I P L H S Y R X Q R M Z Z H F
R R V C C A A J D L O F H S I T T O C S
U E O A G Y R F X N A M R I B C R H A A
I O T N A Q K V U K O R A T E C X E D U
N J I N Z G F J G L I O P W O U N W U G
P S N M P P G A B F B F V Q D E W S X X
```

Pages 16–17
Dog Breed Word Search

```
L P S N O N H S K F S Z T E P P I H W S V T
I B X T D X Z B O R Z O I H D I X R A S H S
P T O P B Z C R E Z U A N H C S D P C I X H
Z A U M T R W M S P L A B R A D O R H W N E
B L U Y N E U J R E N A R A M I E W I V P E
I A P S B I O B E S E T L A M L B J H A X X
D C O K T R W L O P A P I L L O N W Q X G Q
N I O L E R G B M R R T L W F R H P A K I D
U R V K I E A M R P D B R Y E C B V H Q B G
O E W E L T B L T G L E A J F W B T U T F M
H X X S L H N F I D C H R S Y I Q R A N E W
N O B I O S A J O A U G U C S L K B D X L A
A B D J R F S T I M O U N I H S O E P D T K
H G J F S T T P O E A S J M K L T C B Y A K
G O C N I T A K E S J E H N A Y L H O I E I
F D H O A O M D K E O P I E E L O I O R B T
A L O H I C L P W G M Z A K P S A C E U G A
Q L W C Z S A G I N R R Z H R H A M N A N I
I U E I O Q D S T I Z M M O K O E B U U Z D
P B O B Y G G M E K G J W V U Z Y R R T C O
Y Z R B W G H G C E D M T A Z K K S D D E C
K Z W P O O D L E P Q S D N D X D G B T A Z
```

Pages 22–23
Cat Finder

Pages 24–25
Dog Finder

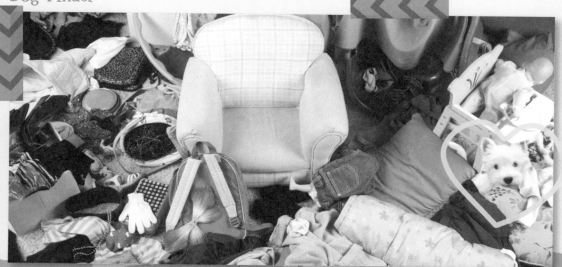

Answers

Pages 82–83
Fetch

Pages 94-95
Kitten Word Scramble

1. yarn
2. fluffy
3. purr
4. hairball
5. Persian
6. bicolor
7. calico
8. tabby
9. meow
10. pampered
11. carrier
12. feline
13. lion
14. tiger
15. catnap
16. exotic
17. litter box
18. mouse

Pages 96-97
Puppy Word Scramble

1. woof
2. bark
3. bone
4. Chihuahua
5. Poodle
6. purebred
7. mutt
8. grooming
9. furry
10. Yorkie
11. treats
12. leash
13. speak
14. bowwow
15. walk
16. collar
17. paw
18. puppy